# Felicity
# FASHION
# STUDIO

# Design Book

★ American Girl®

Questions or comments? Call 1-800-845-0005,
visit our Web site at **americangirl.com**, or write to Customer Service,
American Girl, 8400 Fairway Place, Middleton, WI 53562-0497.

Printed in China
08 09 10 11 12 13 14 15 16 17 LEO 10 9 8 7 6 5 4 3 2 1

PICTURE CREDITS
The following individuals and organizations have generously given permission to reprint illustrations
in this book: p. 15—Colonial Williamsburg Foundation; p. 19—Los Angeles County Museum of Art,
Costume Council Fund; p. 21—Colonial Williamsburg Foundation; p. 22—Los Angeles County
Museum of Art, gift of Mrs. Gabriella K. Robertson and Mrs. Marlene P. L. Toeppen;
p. 24—Colonial Williamsburg Foundation.

Edited by Teri Witkowski
Designed by Carol Moretti
Art directed by Cesca Piuma
Fabric design by Lisa Wilber, Mary Sullivan , and Shelley Cornia
Stencil design by Carol Moretti, Kendra Schluter, and Phillip McKeown
Produced by Jeannette Bailey, Julie Kimmell, Gail Longworth,
Judith Lary, Phillip McKeown, Kendra Schluter, and Sally Wood
Photography by Bob Nardi
Styling by Karen Timm
Illustrations by Dan Andreasen, Susan McAliley, and Randall Berndt

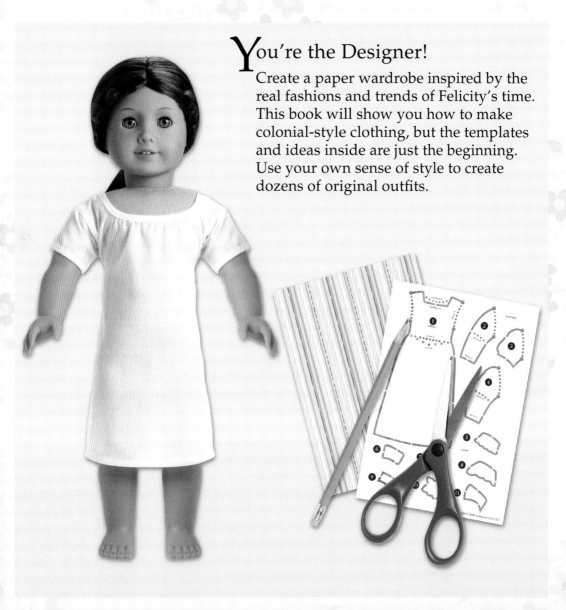

# You're the Designer!

Create a paper wardrobe inspired by the
real fashions and trends of Felicity's time.
This book will show you how to make
colonial-style clothing, but the templates
and ideas inside are just the beginning.
Use your own sense of style to create
dozens of original outfits.

# Tools and Supplies

### Piles of Paper

The paper in your Fashion Studio looks like fabric for clothing that Felicity could have worn in colonial times. All 20 sheets are double-sided, so you'll get two different designs with every piece you create.

### Fashion Stencils

Use the five sheets of fashion stencils to create gowns, jackets, cloaks, and other styles that were popular when Felicity was growing up. Learn how on pages 4 through 7.

### Design Stamp

Create your own fabric pattern with a dainty design stamp. The instructions on page 13 will get you started.

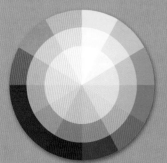

### Color Wheel

Discover how colors work together to create different looks. Use the color wheel on the inside cover to design perfect combinations.

## Paper Doll and Sticky Dots

Dress your Felicity paper doll with the clothes
you create. The reusable sticky dots make it
easy to change clothes and to mix and match
different pieces to create new outfits.

## Accessory Stickers

No outfit is complete
without accessories!
Put the finishing touches
on your fashions with
reusable stickers. The
stickers are uncolored
so that you can create the
perfect shoes, buttons, and
bows to match any outfit.

## You'll also need these supplies:

- Scissors
- Sharp pencil
- Blank paper for sketching
- Felt-tip marker
- Brush-tip marker* for the rubber stamp
- Crayons, colored pencils, or markers for coloring
  the stickers

*Sold at stamping, scrapbooking, or craft stores*

3

# Seven Style Steps

Use the fashion stencils to create clothes for Felicity. Here's how:

1. Choose the stencils you'll need for each outfit. Each stencil is numbered, and the instructions begin on page 15.

2. Pick the paper fabrics you want to use. See pages 10 through 13 for tips on choosing colors and mixing and matching patterns.

3. Place the stencil on top of the paper. Make sure the pattern is turned in the direction you want before you trace the shape.

*You can create different looks by turning the pattern horizontally,*

*vertically,*

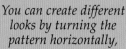

*or diagonally.*

4. Use a pencil to trace along the inside of the stencils.

   Some stencils also have rows of dots. Fill in the dots to create different necklines, waistlines, and sleeve lengths.

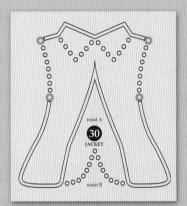

The circles on the stencils indicate where one stencil lines up with another. To make a jacket, trace the lines of stencil 30. Lightly fill in the top and bottom circles where the sleeves will fit.

Now line up the circles of stencil 2 so that the circles you filled in on stencil 30 show through. Trace the lines of the sleeve. Turn stencil 2 over and repeat for the other arm.

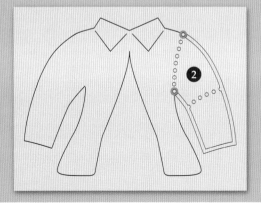

Some of Felicity's gowns have layers of skirts. Adding an *overskirt* is easy.

Trace stencil 1 to make a dress. Lightly fill in the first two circles on both sides of the waist.

Trace stencil 23. You can use the same paper fabric, or you can choose one that's different from the dress.

Cut out the pieces of the overskirt. Now line up the top of the overskirt with the circles at the waist of the dress.

5. Once you've traced all the lines, remove the stencil and cut out the shape. Don't cut too close to the lines yet. Just cut the shape from the sheet of paper.

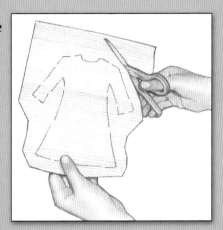

6. Now you can cut along the pencil lines. You'll cut more precisely if you use the center of the scissors rather than the tips.

7. When you've cut out all the pieces, you're ready to put your outfit together. Turn the page for some tips on adding the finishing touches.

# Outfit Assembly

Collars and cuffs are separate pieces. Choose the papers you want to use. Trace the stencils, and cut out the shapes. Use the sticky dots to layer the pieces on top of the gowns.

You'll use stickers for some parts of an outfit. The sticker sheets are uncolored, so you can design each item to match the clothes you've created. The stickers are also removable, so you can add them to all sorts of outfits.

8

## Helpful Hints

- Practice a new outfit on a piece of plain paper before you use the patterned paper.

- Dress the paper doll by placing the sticky dots near the edges of the clothes—such as at the shoulders and waist of a dress. You won't need to use as many dots.

- Ziplock plastic bags are great for storing sticky dots as well as finished outfits and accessories.

*Save the scraps! Those tiny bits of paper make perfect pockets and other decorative details.*

Draw in fold lines and pleats where real fabric would be gathered or bunched. Start with a pencil line, and then fill it in with a felt-tip marker. Don't worry if your outfits don't look exactly like the ones in the book. Make each ensemble uniquely yours!

# Styling Tips—Color

Color has a big impact on an outfit. You can create an entirely different look, even when you use the same clothing pattern, by changing the color combination you choose. Certain colors are more commonly used for fashions in certain seasons. Keep these tips in mind as you design summery gowns, cozy winter cloaks, and everything in between.

*Warm colors,* such as reds, oranges, and yellows, often feel cheerful and lively. Use light colors, like peach and pale yellow, for spring styles. Darker shades of red and gold are perfect for fall fashions.

### Warm Colors

### Cool Colors

Greens, blues, and purples are peaceful and serene *cool colors.* For summer clothes, choose light colors like lavender and sky blue. Build a winter wardrobe around dark shades of purple and green.

*Neutral colors*—gray, black, khaki, and beige—can be paired with practically any color.

*Monochromatic*
(mah-noh-kro-MAT-ick)
color schemes use
lighter and darker
shades of one color.
A little bit of black or
white makes the outfit
interesting.

*Analogous*
(un-AL-luh-gus)
colors are next to one
another on the wheel.
Blue and violet are a
bright combination
that's not too bold.

*Complementary*
colors are opposite
each other on the
wheel. Orange and
blue create a lively
look.

Need some color inspiration? Spin the color wheel inside the front cover
of *Felicity Fashion Studio* as you create your paper fashions.

# Styling Tips—Pattern

Which colors and patterns go together? The choice is yours!
See what happens when you try different combinations.

Match a big print with a small print.
The size contrast will look best if the
patterns share a color scheme.

Put a pattern with a solid color
that appears in the design. Most
prints will also pop with solid
black, white, gray, beige, or navy.

Get creative with the rubber stamp in *Felicity Fashion Studio*.
Trace a stencil shape onto a piece of plain white paper.
Use the stamp to…

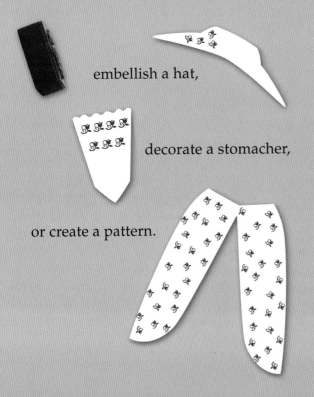

embellish a hat,

decorate a stomacher,

or create a pattern.

For the best stamping results, use a brush-tip
marker instead of an ink pad. Color the raised
portion of the stamp with the marker, and
then stamp the paper.

# Everyday Outfits

In Felicity's time, girls dressed like small versions of their mothers. They wore tightly laced corsets, or *stays*, which gave them stylishly small waists and good posture. Then they put on ankle-length gowns and stockings, shoes with fancy buckles, and hats. Proper colonial women and girls kept their heads covered at all times. Tans and freckles were not at all fashionable!

*For everyday wear, Felicity wore a round-eared cap called a **mob** cap. For dress-up, she wore a lacy cap called a **pinner** cap.*

Jacket: stencils 29, 4A, 8
Skirt: stencil 1 (bottom only), draw gathers
Mob cap: stencil 20, draw gathers
Shoes, bows, and cap ribbon: sticker sheet

## Uncomfortable Undergarments

This humorous illustration shows a woman's stays being laced up. Some women got dizzy or even fainted if their stays were laced too tightly. They simply couldn't get enough air! Felicity didn't like wearing stays because they pinched and itched if she didn't sit perfectly straight and still.

Dress: stencils 1—waist A & neckline B,
3, 10, draw hemlines and gathers
Sash: stencil 28
Hat: stencil 21
Shoes and rosettes: sticker sheet

Dress: stencils 1—waist A & neckline A, 2A, 7,
draw hemlines and gathers
Mob cap: stencil 20, draw gathers
Shoes, choker, and cap ribbon: sticker sheet

*Felicity's apron was attached to her dress with tiny straight pins. Safety pins hadn't been invented yet!*

## Getting Dressed

When Felicity got up in the morning, she laced her *stays* right over the cotton *shift* she'd slept in. Then she tied an *embroidered pocket* around her waist. To make her skirt look full, Felicity sometimes added *pocket hoops*. Next came *stockings*, which were held up with ribbon-like *garters*. She put on a *gown* and finished her outfit with *shoes* and a *cap*.

Dress: stencils 1—waist A & neckline A, 2A, 5
Apron: stencils 13 & 25—waist A, draw gathers
Shoes, hair ribbon, and rosettes: sticker sheet

Dress: stencils 1—waist B & neckline A, 2A,
10, 8, draw gathers
Shoes: sticker sheet

*Hint: Attach
stencil 8 (cuff)
to the sleeve
first, and then
place stencil 10
(ruffle) over it.*

Nightgown: stencils 1—neckline B, 3, 7,
draw gathers
Mob cap: stencil 20, draw gathers
Slippers, bow, and cap ribbon: sticker sheet

Dress: stencils 1—waist B & neckline A,
16, 2A, 10, 8, 23, draw gathers
Shoes and bows: sticker sheet

## Indispensable

Colonial gowns did not
have sewn-in pockets. In
addition to the embroidered
pockets they wore under
their gowns, women and
girls carried small handbags
called *indispensables*. Ladies
wrapped the drawstring
cords around their wrists.

*In the 1770s it was fashionable
to wear skirts with several layers.
To add an **overskirt** to this gown,
follow the directions on page 6.*

# Fancy Fashions

Colonists dressed in their fanciest clothes for special occasions, such as parties and balls. When Felicity received an invitation to a holiday dancing lesson at the Governor's Palace, her mother promised to make her a beautiful new gown. The elegant blue taffeta dress was trimmed with delicate lace. With a satin hair ribbon and dainty dancing slippers, Felicity felt fancy indeed!

## Miniature Mannequins

When Felicity was growing up, most dolls were not playthings. *Milliners*—the owners of clothing shops—used the dolls to show the latest clothing fashions.

Dress: stencils 1—waist B & neckline A,
2A, 16, 9, 8, 23, draw gathers
Hat: stencil 18
Shoes, buttons, ribbon, and bows:
sticker sheet

## Stylish Stomachers

Since colonial girls had few clothes, they often gave an old gown new style by adding a different *stomacher*. The stiff material kept the front of a dress smooth. Like stays, stomachers helped with posture—they made it hard to slouch.

Dress: stencils 1—waist A & neckline A, 2A, 8, 10, 16, 23, draw gathers and rows of ruffles
Shoes and hair ribbon : sticker sheet

Dress: stencils 1—waist B & neckline A, 2A,
9, 8, 16, 23, 34, 24, draw gathers
Shoes and hair ribbon: sticker sheet

Dress: stencils 1—waist A & neckline A,
2A, 11, 8, 15, 23, draw gathers
Mob cap: stencil 20, draw gathers
Shoes, bows, and cap ribbon: sticker sheet

*Felicity wore a stylish **kerchief** wrapped around her shoulders. She fastened it with a small bunch of flowers called a **nosegay**.*

## Pretty and Practical

A fan was a fashionable part of a special-occasion outfit. It was also practical. Fanning cool, fresh air around the head helped women overcome the dizziness they felt from wearing tight corsets.

Dress: stencils 1—waist B & neckline A, 2A, 11, 17, 23, draw gathers
Hat: stencil 18
Shoes, bows, ribbons, and rosette: sticker sheet

Dress: stencils 1—waist B & neckline B, 2A, 9, 8, 14, 23, 24, 34, draw gathers
Shoes, bows, and hair ribbon: sticker sheet

Dress: stencils 1—waist B & neckline B, 2A, 8, 12
Apron: stencil 25—waist B, draw gathers
Mob cap: stencil 20, draw gathers
Shoes, rosette, and cap ribbon: sticker sheet

# Outdoor Outfits

Felicity borrowed a pair of Ben's *breeches*, or knee-length pants, so that she could run to Jiggy Nye's pasture and secretly visit the horse she had named Penny. Felicity was amazed at how free she felt without her long petticoats. Climbing fences and riding horses was so much easier without long skirts! But colonial girls *always* wore ankle-length gowns, even when they played outdoors.

Top: stencil 1 (top only)—waist B
Jacket: stencils 30—waist A, 2B, 6, draw trim
Skirt: stencil 1 (skirt only)—waist B,
draw gathers
Hat: stencil 26, draw trim
Shoes and buttons: sticker sheet

## Riding Like a Lady

Because Felicity wore
a skirt while riding, it
was proper for her to sit
sidesaddle. Both of her
legs had to be on the same
side of the horse. Some-
times staying on could
be tricky!

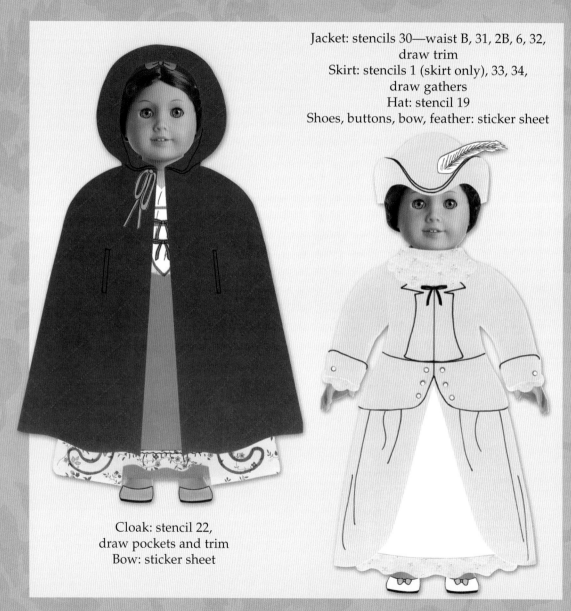

Jacket: stencils 30—waist B, 31, 2B, 6, 32,
draw trim
Skirt: stencils 1 (skirt only), 33, 34,
draw gathers
Hat: stencil 19
Shoes, buttons, bow, feather: sticker sheet

Cloak: stencil 22,
draw pockets and trim
Bow: sticker sheet

## Cold Weather Warm-Ups

To keep out the chilly winter winds, Felicity wrapped up in her warm wool cloak. She wore fingerless leather gloves called *mitts* to keep her arms warm, and she tucked her hands into her satin *muff*.

Cloak: stencil 22—neckline A, draw pockets and trim
Bow: sticker sheet

# Show Off Your Style

Have fun with your fashions. Mix and match the stencils to design the outfits you'd like to model on your Felicity paper doll. Make a simple summer dress, or create a fancy ball gown. Design your own fashionable riding habit. There's no limit to your imagination!

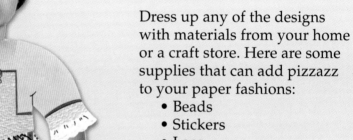

Dress up any of the designs with materials from your home or a craft store. Here are some supplies that can add pizzazz to your paper fashions:

- Beads
- Stickers
- Lace
- Felt
- Buttons
- Ribbon
- Cording
- Glitter
- Feathers